# Contents

*C = copper; B = bronze; ( ) = the line must be played but cannot be assessed for a Medal.

# Tutti Fluty

Paul Harris

AB 3020

# Reflections

Gordon Lewin

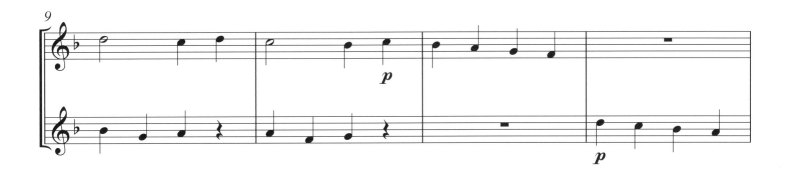

# Duet in Paris

Sally Adams

AB 3020

# Cry from Within

Robert Tucker

# Blackberry and Apple Crumble

Paul Harris

AB 3020

# Road-Hogs

Sally Adams

# London Bridge is falling down

Trad. English arr. Alan Haughton

# Take it or leave it!

Paul Harris

# Setting Off

Howard Dyer

AB 3020

# The Lonely Hamster

Pam Wedgwood

# Theme from Symphony No. 9

Beethoven arr. Mark Goddard

AB 3020

# Not Now!

Sarah Watts

# Stepping on Stones

Colin Cowles

AB 3020

# Da Da Dance

Philip Mundey

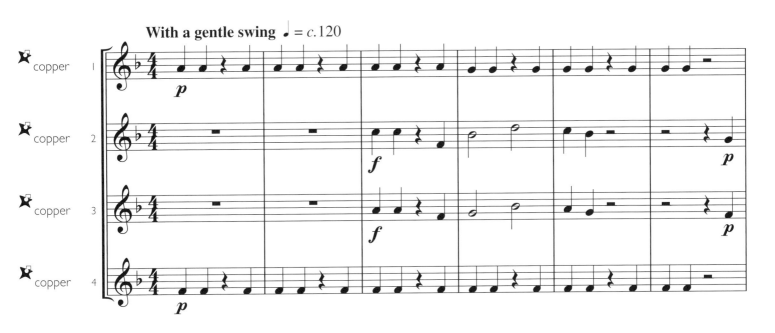

# Daisy Chain

Sarah Watts

AB 3020

# Sea Mist

Sally Adams

# Song of the Plains

Kit Turnbull

AB 3020

# Hallelujah Chorus

from *Messiah*

Handel arr. Mark Goddard

AB 3020     03/12